Harry Potter™

MAGICAL
PLACES & CHARACTERS
COLOURING BOOK

STUDIO PRESS

An Insight Editions Book

The world we journey through in the Harry Potter films is magical and extraordinary. From a bank run by goblins to a castle filled with staircases that move, we are continually taken to new and incredible places. We follow a young boy who has discovered a world he never knew existed and we encounter there a thrilling cast of wizards, witches and so much more. The pages that follow are an invitation to relive the magic of the Harry Potter films and bring your own vibrant colours to the wizarding world outlined here in black and white.

ART CREDITS:
Hogwarts castle, herbology classroom, library, Burrow, and escape from Gringotts concept art by Andrew Williamson. Prefect's bathroom window and Quidditch pitch concept art by Adam Brockbank. Death Eater masks by Rob Bliss.

Produced by

INSIGHT EDITIONS
PO Box 3088
San Rafael, CA 94912

www.insighteditions.com

PUBLISHER: Raoul Goff
ART DIRECTOR: Chrissy Kwasnik
COVER DESIGN & LAYOUT: Jenelle Wagner
EXECUTIVE EDITOR: Vanessa Lopez
PROJECT EDITOR: Greg Solano
PRODUCTION EDITOR: Rachel Anderson
PRODUCTION MANAGER: Blake Mitchum
JUNIOR PRODUCTION MANAGER: Alix Nicholaeff
PRODUCTION COORDINATOR: Leeana Diaz

INSIGHT EDITIONS would like to thank Victoria Selover, Elaine Piechowski, and Melanie Swartz.

ILLUSTRATIONS BY Adam Raiti, Robin F. Williams, Maxime Lebrun, Dee Pei, Frans Boukas, Britt Wilson, and Manuel Martinez.

ROOTS of PEACE ✦ REPLANTED PAPER

Insight Editions, in association with Roots of Peace, will plant two trees for each tree used in the manufacturing of this book. Roots of Peace is an internationally renowned humanitarian organization dedicated to eradicating land mines worldwide and converting war-torn lands into productive farms and wildlife habitats. Roots of Peace will plant two million fruit and nut trees in Afghanistan and provide farmers there with the skills and support necessary for sustainable land use.

Manufactured in Italy by Insight Editions